SHERLOCK HOLMES

THE RED DEATH

A. CONAN DOYLE

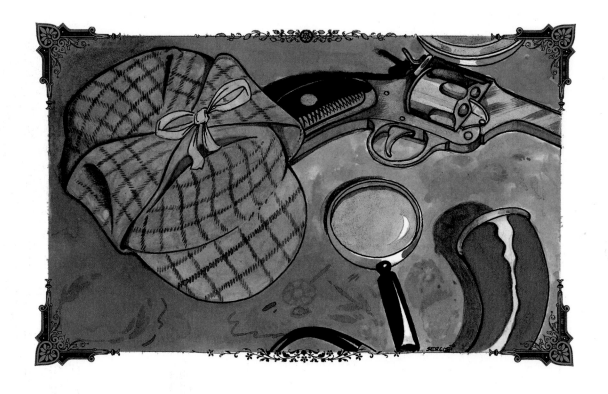

Adaptation:
A.-P. DUCHÂTEAU

Illustration:
G. CLAIR

RAVETTE BOOKS

Translated from the original story
La Sangsue Rouge
A. Conan Doyle – A. -P. Duchâteau – G Clair
© 1990 Claude Lefrancq Editeur

Rights gained from Yaffa Character Licensing

This edition first published by Ravette Books Limited 1992

Printed and bound for Ravette Books Limited,
3 Glenside Estate, Star Road, Partridge Green,
Horsham, West Sussex RH13 8RA
An Egmont Company
by Proost International Bookproduction, Belgium

ISBN: 1 85304 463 6

It was one of those evenings when my friend Sherlock Holmes seemed determined to live up to the image I have portrayed of him in my simple little stories. . .

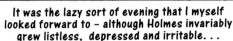

It was the lazy sort of evening that I myself looked forward to – although Holmes invariably grew listless, depressed and irritable. . .

Oh. I beg of you, Watson! I'd be grateful if you could avoid using that odious little phrase 'And they lived happily ever after'!

Pardon? What. . . ?

MR HOLMES! MR HOLMES!

You were staring at an article in 'The Times': Colonel Warburton has taken leave of his senses and killed his wife. You shook your head two or three times and then absent-mindedly looked at the picture of the young woman – and back at her husband again. .

What is the matter, my dear Mrs Hudson?

There's a man. . . on the front door steps . . . he can hardly stand up. . . I think he's dying . . . he keeps repeating your name. . .

AARGH AARGH

Watson! This man is seriously ill. . . Call a doctor, quickly!

But. . . I AM a doctor!

Holmes! You must save me from THE RED DEATH!

SB 1

He's delirious!

Help me, Watson! Let's take him to your room! You can examine him there and look after him!...

One moment! What's this? A cutting from the 'Strand' magazine!

Who could have been foolish enough to put an advertisement like this in the 'Strand'?

TO WHOM IT MAY CONCERN
If you need help, contact:
Sherlock Holmes
221B Baker Street, London

Just let me explain, Holmes! It won't take...

Not now, Watson! First let's look after this unemployed, short-sighted actor who specialises in provincial tours!

Holmes! I'm flabbergasted!

No. Watson! Just common sense! Now I wonder... those shoes!... Look after him, Watson! I won't be long!

It's rainy and muddy out... yet his boots were almost dry, and hardly had a mark on them!

OF COURSE!
He was brought here in a carriage

SR3

He's already lost a lot of blood . . . Let's hope we can still save him!

Hm! If we put the impossible to one side. What we have left – however unlikely it may be – is the SOLUTION!

Let us imagine that someone standing in the shadows cracked the whip, and the horse has been trained to take me. . . somewhere!

THE. . . THE RED LEECH! IT'S VILE!. . . LOATHSOME!! IT'S EVERYWHERE!

Take it easy, now! We're going to try and get you well again!

Holmes isn't back yet! Have a look out of the window, Mrs Hudson, would you? See if he's coming!

Very well, Dr. Watson!

Well?

Not a soul! The street's empty!

The phantom coachman is cracking his whip again! Aha! I see! This time, we're stopping!

SHLAAK

?!

HAAAAH

Do you see, Mrs Hudson?

Ugh! No! It's too disgusting for words, Doctor! You should know better than to ask a lady to. . .!

I'm sorry! Just a manner of speaking! What I meant was. . . Well, anyway, I've removed the leeches from the poor man's body – he was covered in them! But he's still in a very serious condition. . . VERY SERIOUS INDEED!

. . . Master of the Red Death. . . M. . . Master of the In. . . Invisible . . .

He's delirious again! In my opinion, Holmes has got it wrong! I think this fellow's a servant – someone's butler perhaps.

PUF PUF

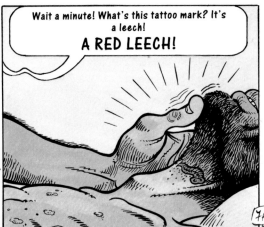

Wait a minute! What's this tattoo mark? It's a leech!

A RED LEECH!

So I'm a murderer, am I, Inspector?

I made a blunder, Mr Holmes! I apologise! Lord Brewster is not dead . . . he has just lost consciousness!

My poor love! You need some rest!

My humblest apologies! It's all very peculiar, but. . .

. . . but you were probably sent a message saying a crime was about to be committed at 'The Cedars' – and that I was the culprit!

Exactly! But how. . . ?

The red cab! Did you see a red cab?

G. CLAIR A.F. DUCHÂTEAU

Oh, why not? You only live once! . . . don't want to HIC go home. . . not yet anyway. . . I want ADVENTURE! . . .

I thought I was dreaming. The invisible coachman cracked his whip and the horse set off. . .

SHLAAK

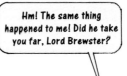

Hm! The same thing happened to me! Did he take you far, Lord Brewster?

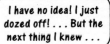

I have no idea! I just dozed off! . . . But the next thing I knew . . .

Hurrah! We're here!

HOUPS!

9A)

?

There seemed to be a seat waiting for me at one of the gaming tables. . . I eased myself into it!

And then. . . oh! . . . the HORROR! the RUIN!

9B)

In the space of one depraved evening, I signed away my fortune and my honour.

I lost everything we own – I even had to sign an acknowledgement of my debts . . . in my own blood!

My love! There's the money I inherited! Take it all! It's YOURS!

No, Violet! No! I couldn't do a thing like that!

Now you know everything, Mr Holmes! They . . They have condemned me to death! When the cab with the invisible coachman stopped outside the house, it meant one thing. . my EXECUTION!

. . . and you took me for your executioner!

This case is already a tricky one! You see how they managed to bring me here in the hope that we would kill one another!

But . . . I don't follow you!

Tell me, do you have in your employ a man who wears spectacles and looks a little like that actor. . .

Oh. yes! That's Dale, our butler! He came to work for us a few weeks ago!

He had an excellent reference from . . . who was it now? . . .

. . . May I see the letter, Lady Brewster?

I'll go and get it. . .

I hereby declare that Mr Dale has been a trustworthy and loyal servant. Professor Moriarty

G. CLAIR – A.P. DUCHATEAU –

Later on, back at Baker Street

Moriarty alive! Back from the dead?! It's impossible Holmes! You managed to escape with your life at the Falls of Reichenbach, but Moriarty......

Moriarty is the criminal genius of all time! He is capable of anything!...

That unemployed actor, Dale – short-sighted fellow, specialised in provincial tours!...

How did you guess that, Holmes?

How many more times, Watson? I never guess! A reddish mark near his nose told me that Dale usually wore glasses... and some traces of powder and eye shadow suggested to me that he had been made to play the part of a butler...

.. But his skin was puckered as if he often used make up! I then thought he might be an actor – not a very good one – probably doing provincial towns. At all events. Moriarty probably ordered him... to find work in Lord Brewster's household...

The poor man must have betrayed the criminal organisation of the Red Leech, which then took its cruel revenge _ and he only came to me after he saw the advertisement in the 'Strand'.

We had to take him off to hospital, Holmes! He's not in his right mind any more!...

I was looking forward to a quiet, relaxed evening at home, Watson, but I'm afraid we still have work to do! Put your coat on, and make sure you bring a firearm with you!

11A

11B

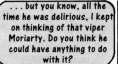

Let's go and have a look inside. Watson! Perhaps it'll be full of ghosts!

You don't believe that people can make themselves invisible, do you?

Well, you know, the American writer Edgar Allan Poe has published something about it, and over here the young novelist H. G. Wells is currently writing a book – called 'The Invisible Man'!

I don't like the look of this place one bit!

The gamblers are wearing masks!. . . but at least they're not invisible!

15A

Excuse me, Sir!. . . I don't believe you're a member of the 'Red Leech' club. . .

SO HOP IT!

I know your face! Yes. . . you're Bonny the Bull! You were a fine boxer in your day, but unfortunately you took to the bottle. . .

HOLMES! THE BLOKE FROM SCOTLAND YARD! I'M GOING TO. . . !

15B

Holmes! That man's as strong as an ox! Let me take over – there's a good chap – otherwise. . .

No! Let me play with him for a moment, Watson! It's all part of the investigation.

Well, Bonny! Still playing by the Queensbury Rules? Or don't you go in for that sort of thing anymore?

What's that got to do with you. . Ouch!. . Yeah! I. . . oof!. . . still fight clean!

THUD THUD

That's all I wanted to know, my dear chap! Sorry to have to terminate this little interlude, but. . .

. . . I'm in a HURRY!

SMACK

AAN

16A

This is serious gambling!

Don't be fooled by the elaborate masks, though! Behind each one lurks an aristocrat leading a double life – and a squalid, seedy life at that!. . .

16B

But frightened by the blackout and choked by the fumes, the masked gamblers ran for their lives. . .

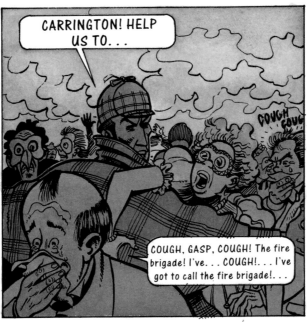

Then suddenly. . .

But the terrified, panic-stricken gamblers ignore the advice, and take to their heels. Holmes and Watson are pushed and shoved and jostled.

. . . and then bundled to one side.

Anyone who slips is immediately trampled underfoot. . .

Later, when the police arrive, and the fire brigade comes to put out the fire. . .

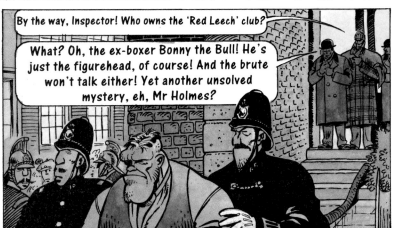

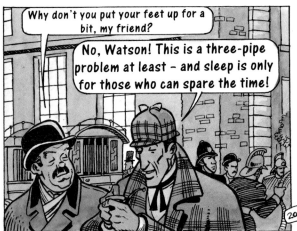

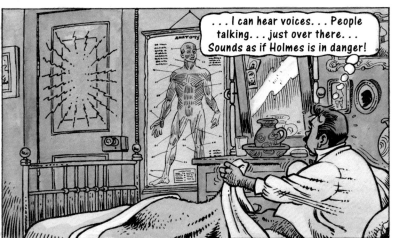

!?

HANDS UP!

It's all right, my friend! You can put your gun away or we'll have an accident! Everything is under control! I think you will recognise our young assistants, the Baker Street irregulars! They were just leaving, in fact!

Oh. . . I. . . I thought. . .

HA! HA! HA! HA!

Now. I'm relying on you to come up with some information on Dale. . . where theatre folk meet, the club – that sort of thing!

Righto! Mr Holmes!

Well, Watson! Are you beginning to see a light at the end of the tunnel?

Not really, Holmes!

You see, if Moriarty has really re-turned from the dead, he'll find it very difficult to build up his crime empire again! He's going to need money – a lot of money! THAT is why he's going for the aristo. . .

MR HOLMES! MR HOLMES!

Mrs Hudson! Please don't tell me there are any more people dying on my front door step!

Mr Holmes! It's horrible! Just outside the house. . . a red cab. . . and inside! . . .

?

Hm! I'm afraid there's nothing I can do for him. . .

Don't talk nonsense, Watson! HE'S ALIVE!

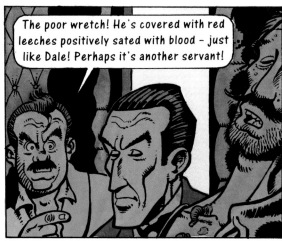

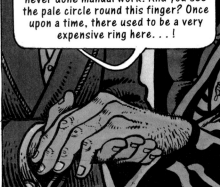

23A

23B

SCHLAAAK AAAARGH!

He's fallen off!... Better stop my horse before...

OH! OH!

He's got up again! There he goes!

24A

Which way did he go? He must have run off up this drive...

But... the place is DESERTED! And yet this is the only way he could have come!

24B

WE SHALL MEET AGAIN HOLMES! YOU THOUGHT YOU TRIUMPHED AT THE FALLS OF REICHENBACH! YOU WERE WRONG! REVENGE WILL BE MINE!

I don't believe it! I could have sworn. . .
HE MUST BE HERE!

In. . . Invisible. . . with no b. . . body at all! . . .

It is most mysterious. . . I would be grateful, though, Lord Brewster. . . Carrington. . . , if you could identify the Red Death's latest victim. . .

Any time, Holmes!

Of course!

The two red cabs have vanished

We can go in mine, Holmes!

26A

Later, in Baker Street. . .

And how is our mystery invalid coming along?

Same as Dale. I'm afraid – delirium, fever. . .

Lord Brewster, Carrington! Do you know this man?

I'll say I do!

26B

What?

It's the Grand Duke!... Holmes! Watson! You must do everything you can to save this man's life!

Grand Duke?

May I introduce you to GRAND DUKE SERGEI ITCHKIN, one of the Tsar's most trusted associates! He's been in this country for several months on a diplomatic mission!

Do you mean to say that?...

I'm beginning to see, Lord Reginald, that this business of getting you to acknowledge your gambling debts is one of Moriarty's more sinister tricks!

Now, let me think... did you... er.. by any chance first meet Grand Duke Sergei Itchkin at the... er... 'Red Leech'?

I'm afraid so... and he was playing for high stakes – VERY HIGH INDEED!

Presumably he signed the acknowledgement of his debts with his own blood... and then had to default!

27A

How dreadful! If this got out, it would lead to a huge political scandal!

Yes, and the effect on diplomatic relations with Russia would be catastrophic!

Mrs Hudson! What's troubling you? Can I be of assistance?

Somebody else with red leeches arriving in a mysterious cab?

There are two gentlemen waiting to see you, sir... Two gentlemen... it's a confidential matter, you understand...

That's all right, Mrs Hudson! Show Mr Brown and Mr Smith in immediately!

How do you know those were their names?

Were you expecting these two gentlemen to visit us, Holmes?

Not in the least, Watson, but they wish our meeting to be confidential... moreover, Smith and Brown are the most commonly assumed names in such circumstances...

IN THE NAME OF HOLY RUSSIA! LET NO ONE MOVE!

!?

27B

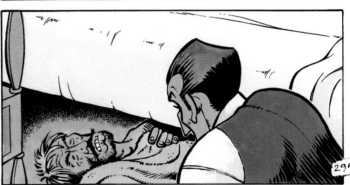

One hour later, as I watched my friend, Sherlock Holmes, carefully remove the top of his sixth boiled egg...

Healthy appetite this morning, I see!...

What a remarkably astute observation, Watson!

!

You can't play the violin at this time! You'll wake up all the neighbours!

You know perfectly well, Watson, that it helps me to concentrate!

It might help you, but what about me?

Which is better? Me being able to concentrate or you NOT being able to concentrate?

How many times have I told you not to burst in like that without?...

That's all right. Watson! I'm sure they've got something very interesting to tell us!

CRYSTAL PALACE
— PRESENTS —
DALE DALE
THE ENTERTAINER
SCOTTY
THE VENTRILOQUIST

Incredible! You were right all along, Holmes!... Dale really was a third-rate music hall performer!

Exactly, and...

LOOK OUT, HOLMES!

Humph! It's the old story of Colonel Moran and his airgun all over again!

Yes, they've even rented a flat across the road from us like last time, do you see?...

...except they didn't use an airgun this time, though! They used a bow and arrow! What a charmingly old-fashioned way of delivering a message!

I didn't die, Holmes, during our struggle at the Falls of Reichenbach – any more than you did! Yet again, we are one too many! We must resolve our little problem! I will be waiting for you at eleven o'clock this evening at Mackleton railway station in the north of England.

Moriarty

Don't go, Holmes! It's bound to be a trap!

Moriarty is alive! The Napoleon of crime! the evil monster! It is my duty, Holmes, to accept his challenge!

But it seems he can make himself invisible!

So can I... when I'm in the mood, Holmes!

32A

That evening at Mackleton Station...

MACKLETON STATION

NEWS

SLIG SLIG

32B

I put on a brave face for Watson's sake, but if Moriarty can REALLY make himself invisible, I've got myself into a bit of a pickle...

...Like me, that evil genius is brilliant at disguises... I need to be on my guard against the people I can see as well as the people I can't see!

The place is deserted! No one around! Now does that mean Moriarty is here or not?

What's this? A train coming? But there aren't supposed to be any more trains till tomorrow!

!

Red carriage, of course!... And 'M' for Moriarty – I might have guessed!

Well, I'll be!... That door's opening... like an invitation to jump on board... Now where on earth could this ghost train be taking me...?

BANG!
BANG!

...HA HA!...

BANG

HA HA

HO! HO! HO!

Later...

And he just ran off into the night, even though I'd shot him three times!

Perhaps your hand was shaking, Holmes!

No! That's impossible! I took careful aim each time!

Hum!

You don't believe me, do you?... But wait a moment!... Who has got the train moving again? WHO?

I don't... er...

This demon seems to have power over events – or over machines, anyway! I'm...

Holmes! Carrington!

First, they made a great show of leaving. Then...

Coachman! Wait for us here! Let's go straight back to the house, Watson!

Are you worried about what is going on back there?

Yes. I am! I only just had time to whisper a few words into Lord Reginald's ear...

We waited and waited, my teeth chattering with fear, while my celebrated companion retained his icy cool.

Suddenly...

HELP! HELP!

BLAM!

Who was that crying out?... And those gun shots?... I hope I haven't miscalculated...

Locked!...

THUD THUD

40A

OPEN UP! HOLMES HERE!

Thank goodness you've come, Mr Holmes! The man... the invisible man ...he's got into the house somehow...

He gave my husband a terrible fright, but Carrington chased him off!

40B

The blighter got away, Holmes!

How is Lord Reginald?

He's lost consciousness!. . . He had a terrible shock. . . Perhaps he's coming round. . .

I. . . I can hear you, Holmes!

I. . . I need to rest. . . rest. . . but if it's the last thing you do, Holmes, save me from the RED DEATH!

Trust me, Lord Reginald!

Is he safe in this room, Mr Holmes? I've closed the shutters, and there's only one door. . .

. . . and we'll lock that! What about the chimney, though?

I have an idea! We'll keep the fire burning! Not even the devil would try and get in that way!

That should do it! We've locked the door, and we're not going to let the key out of our sight! Perhaps you'd like to rest a little as well, Lady Violet. . . Carrington?

I'll stay here with you, if you don't mind!

Same here!

So nobody can get into the room, then! A detective problem for the connoisseur, eh, what? Watson?

Yes, and I'll be fascinated to see how Moriarty tries to solve it, Holmes!

Open up! IT'S ME, MYCROFT!

?

Mycroft! He'd only have come in an emergency! I'll go and let him in, but keep your eyes on the door, Watson, whatever else you do!

You can trust me!

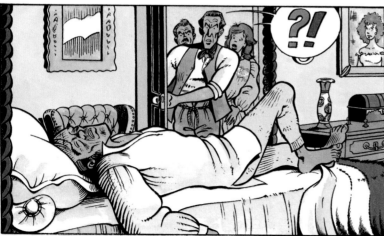

What?

Yes, Watson! Lady Violet and Carrington had this fiendish plan for getting their hands on the fortunes of rich members of the aristocracy – **and starting with Lord Reginald!**

The Grand Duke and others were all brought to the 'Red Leech' – the tables were rigged, of course. Those who refused to pay up, and anyone who tried to expose them were tortured by thirsty leeches – that was doubtless the fate of poor Dale the music hall artiste turned butler!

What about Moriarty! He's kidnapped the Prime Minister! Don't you understand?

Moriarty was pulling the strings – the others were mere puppets who did as they were told! His ultimate aim was to destabilise the British Government at a critical moment!...

Sherlock! The Prime Minister – we've got to find him!

All in good time! You'll find he's being held by Moriarty and Moran... in a place guarded by the police where no one would dream of looking!...

...And that reminds me, Mycroft! Tell Inspector Lestrade to come and arrest these two crooks, will you?

Reginald! Please listen to me! It was all a terrible mistake... I do love you!

44A

Please forgive...

I wonder what you would have done if you had hated me! You were after my money, that's all! Don't worry, Holmes! They won't get away! They can wait here until Lestrade and his men get here...

Later...

44

Why here, Holmes?

It's obvious! This place is locked and guarded! What better hiding place?

We'll have to be on our guard – don't forget Moriarty is invisible!

Ha! Ha! He's no more invisible than you or I, Watson!

Mr. Holmes!

Ah! You know who I am! Be so good as to break these seals... AND COME WITH ME!

44c

45

G. CLAIRG 90.

46A

END